By Elizabeth Krych
Illustrations by Kelly Kennedy

SCHOLASTIC INC.
New York Toronto London Auckland
Sydney Mexico City New Delhi Hong Kong

To Nicole,
best friend at Halloween and all year long.
– E. K.

ISBN 978-0-545-36561-1

12 11 10 9 8 7 6 5 4 3 2 1 11 12 13 14 15 16/0

Printed in the U.S.A. 40
First Scholastic printing, October 2011
Design by Becky Terhune

Table of Contents

STINKY ZOMBIE
ISBN 978-0-545-38144-4
REST IN PIECES

INVITATION

Come to our zombie party
In the graveyard at midnight.
All the undead we've invited
Are sure to be a sight!

We zombies are so friendly,
Bring all your pals along.
Don't be afraid of our parade,
Come join in our song!

The ghosts do karaoke
(They are such a lively bunch).
A mummy raps, a vampire naps
Until the werewolves bring the punch.

A phantom DJ's spinning
Until the nighttime wanes.
Then at dawn, when the guests have gone,
You won't even miss your brains!

R.I.P.

Raking Regrets

I love leaves changing colors,
And the crinkling sound they make.
I love jumping in leaf piles,
But how I hate to rake!

If only leaves dropped neatly,
And the fall winds blew less hard,
I wouldn't spend my Saturday
De-leafing my backyard!

Apple Time Rhyme

In the orchard, me and you shall
Soon fill up a basket bushel.

Idared and Jonamac,
Munching on an apple snack.

Red Delicious, McIntosh,
Cooking up some applesauce.

Granny Smith and Northern Spy,
Baking in an apple pie.

Braeburn, Cortland, Fuji, too—
Please, take some apples home with you!

Dead End

At my street's end, there's a house
Where only weeds are planted.
With sagging steps and a creaking gate,
It's perfect to be haunted.

For ghosts won't mind the drafts, you see,
Or the crumbling chimney pile,
Broken panes and missing doors
Are just those tenants' style.

So if you see some eerie lights,
And hear spooky sounds that aren't the wind,
There's a good chance the house is rented,
And ghost neighbors have moved in!

My Black Cat

My cat is black as licorice,
As dark as ink or coal,
She sneaks around the neighborhood
Like an invisible patrol.

When slinking through the shadows,
She disappears from sight.
But she comes when I call her—
Can you guess her name? Midnight!

Scaredy-Bat

A bat and an owl
Went for a flight
Under a Halloween moon,
But a werewolf howl
Gave them a fright
And they returned home very soon.

"I fear," said the bat,
As he hung upside down,
"We should find somewhere else to be working.
For it's certain that
In this part of town
Some bigger night creatures are lurking!"

The Scariest Thing in My Closet

It's moldy, furry, dusty,
And a gruesome shade of green,
It's the very last piece of candy
Left over from last Halloween!

Lost and Found

A
Hat
That is
Pointed
Like a black
Ice-cream cone
Appeared in our lost and found
Box this week. It seems so familiar, but whose
Could it be? This black hat, with its broad
Brim and sharp peak?

TEST

Veggie Vampire

I'm a vegetarian vampire,
So broccoli, beware!
I'm a terror to tomatoes
And a carrot's worst nightmare.

I cannot stand the sight of blood,
But just to keep you guessing,
I might eat the veggies off your plate
And *you* for salad dressing!

The Spooky Rules

Don't unwrap a mummy,
And don't hide a witch's broom.
Never pet a werewolf,
And don't tap-dance on a tomb.
Ghosts shouldn't be short-sheeted,
Never unplug Frankenstein,
Because I'm a big, scary monster,
And they're all friends of mine!

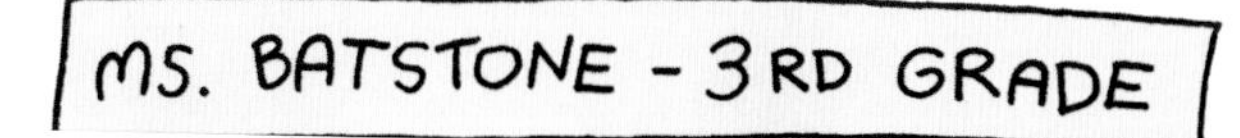

The Forbidden Chamber

There's a monster in my cellar,
Where I almost dare not go.
Eerie music and weird laughter
Echo from the fiend below.

Odd smells float up the stairway,
So be sure to hold your nose.
Like stinky socks, a pizza box,
And a heap of unwashed clothes.

Take care to walk on tiptoe
As you peer into the gloom—
Who knows what strange things are lurking
In my big brother's room?

STINKY ZOMBIE

ISBN 978-0-545-38145-1

Hayride

When the autumn sky is clear
And like a golden apple is the sun,
We take a trip, like every year,
Out for some country fun.

Farmer Herman drives the tractor
On a pumpkin patch hayride
With lots of cheerful laughter
We bring back pumpkins at our side.

In the barn, we feed the horses
And our grins grow wider
As we end our farmyard afternoon
With a doughnut and some cider.

The Halloween Bully

The Halloween bully on our street
Sure can spoil my celebration.
Chocolate, gum, and any sweet
Is fair game for confiscation.

On every October thirty-first
My friends all run in fear
When that big shadow that means the worst
Beneath a streetlight does appear.

Last year, the bully demanded
I surrender all my loot,
And I came home empty-handed
(With just a toothbrush and some fruit)

But this time I'll be brave enough
At last to stare that bully down,
In her fairy princess costume
And her matching plastic crown.

Witches' Stew
Two crocodile tears from down the Nile,
Ogre's blood (a big, full vial),
Whiskers from three big black cats,
A dozen tails of subway rats,
Heaping scoop of monster mash,
Dried poison ivy (just a dash).
Stir all together with long-handled spoon.
Let simmer in light of Halloween moon.
Serve shrieking hot once flavor blends.
Slurp and enjoy with a dozen good friends!
OGRE BLOOD
GARLIC

MELLY MONSTER
R.I.P.
PEACE

To My Ghoulfriend

Roses are dead,
Violets are, too.
Skunks are smelly,
And so are you.

Nettles and thorns,
Stinkweed and burrs,
Make this bouquet
Perfectly yours.

Your hair is lank,
Your skin is green,
So please be mine
This Halloween!

Halloween Haiku

When October comes
Trees are costumed like kids, too.
Red, yellow, orange.

On a chilly night
The big harvest moon watches
Like an owl's eye.

The morning after
Jack-o'lanterns grin at dawn
And greet November.

My Favorite Candy

Some kids like Easter jelly beans,
Some Hanukkah gelt prefer.
Candy canes and gingerbread
Others like best, I'm sure.

But there's a special magic
You can't taste in those sweets,
A Halloweeny flavor
Only found in trick-or-treats!

CANDY
CHOCOLATE

The Unsuccessful Scarecrow

Two arms, two legs,
Old overalls,
We stuffed them all with straw.
Then a checked shirt
And mismatched boots,
But somewhere there's a flaw.

A floppy hat
And smiling face
Finished up our man of hay,
But this fellow
Looks so friendly
He can't scare anything away!

Candy Garden

I planted my trick-or-treat candy,
Each chocolate bar and lollipop,
And when it's ripe, next Halloween,
I'll harvest my candy corn crop!

LICORICE

GARLIC

CHOCOLATE

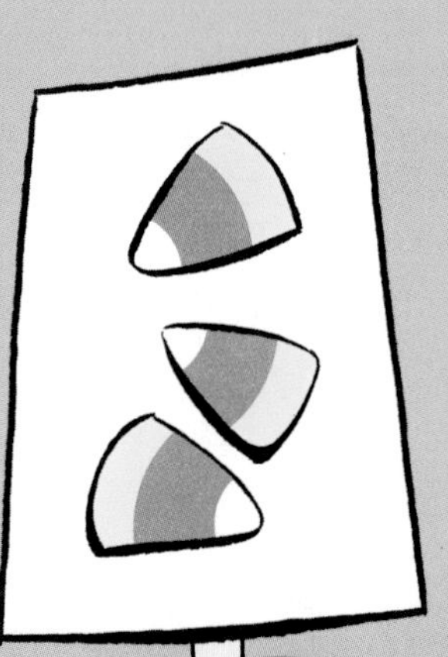

Trick or Treat?

PUMPKIN

Pumpkins, pumpkins,
Burning bright
In the dark October night.
You growl and glare,
But we're delighted
To see your flaming faces lighted.

Children, children,
Trick-or-treat
On our decorated street.
Pirate, cowgirl,
Mummy, and queen,
Be safe and brave this Halloween!